In Ravi's Den

Written by Jon Tovey

Illustrated by Shelagh McNicholas

Ravi was in his den.

"This is no fun," he said.

"I'll go and get my cars."

Ravi played with his cars.

"This is no fun," he said.

"I'll go and get my plane."

Ravi played with his plane.

"This is no fun," he said.
"I'll go and get my rocket."

Ravi played with his rocket.

"This is no fun," he said.
"I'll go and get...

...my friend Paul."

Ravi and Paul played in the den all day.